AFTER
A FEW

Reg Smythe

ꓤꓤ
RAVETTE BOOKS

This edition first published by Ravette Books Limited 1992.

Printed and bound
for Ravette Books Limited
3 Glenside Estate, Star Road, Partridge Green,
Horsham, West Sussex RH13 8RA
An Egmont Company
by Stige Arti Grafiche, Italy

ISBN: 1 85304 397 4

'OW DO YOU FEEL ABOUT A LASS WI' THE COURAGE TO STAND UP *TO* YOU?!

BAR

ANYTHING IN A SKIRT THAT SMILES AT HIM!

— C'MON, PUT 'EM UP! YOU NEED TAKING DOWN A PEG — AND I'M JUST THE KID TO DO IT—!

—WELL?

A WORD OF ADVICE, CHALKIE — DON'T BEAT HIM AT SNOOKER TONIGHT

COME RIGHT IN AND LET'S HEAR IT-!

ALWAYS MORE THAN READY TO SHOOT DOWN ANY EXCUSE I CARE TO OFFE. - BUT TONIGHT I GET MY OWN BACK-

7-17

7-24

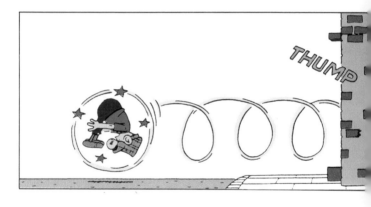

SORRY I'M LATE, FOLKS. HOPE YOU ARE ALL ENJOYING YOURSELVES—

WHENEVER WE THROW A PARTY, IT'S ALWAYS THE SAME OLD ARGUMENT WITH *HER* LOT — WHO INVITED THE HOST!

HEY! YOU! COME HERE —

IT'S USUALLY THE SHADY-LADY TYPE WHO BRINGS A BIT OF SUNSHINE INTO THAT LAD'S LIFE

10-16

I'VE HEARD ALL ABOUT YOU TONIGHT! YOU'RE GETTING NO SUPPER, NO MATTER HOW YOU CREATE~!

WHERE HAVE YOU BEEN?

FAIR ENOUGH, PET

IT MIGHT DO IF YOU DIDN'T ALWAYS PRAY FOR MORE THINGS THAN *YOU'RE* WILLING TO WORK FOR!

ANYONE WHO THINKS THAT THE ART OF CONVERSATION IS DEAD OUGHT TO HAVE A GO AT TELLING *THAT* LAD TO PUSH OFF AT CLOSING TIME

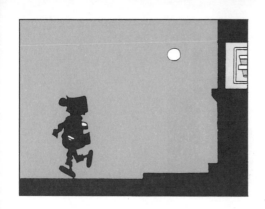

YOU CAN PUT MY SUPPER ON THE TABLE, DEAR. I'VE ONLY GOT TO LOCK UP THEN I'VE FINISHED

WHAT ABOUT CAPP —ANY PROBLEMS?

NONE AT ALL. HE PUSHED OFF ON HIS OWN ACCORD FOR ONCE—

I MISSED THE LAST BUS, JACK. I'LL HAVE THE USUAL WHILE YOU TRY AND GET ME A CAB

THAT'S LIFE. PROBLEMS THAT GO AWAY BY THEMSELVES USUALLY COME BACK BY THEMSELVES

1-15

READY
WHEN
YOU
ARE —

© 1984 M.G.N.
DIST. BY SYNDICATION INTERNATIONAL NORTH
AMERICA SYNDICATE INC.

≶SIGH≶

IT'S A HARD LIFE AT MY AGE.
YOU'RE CONSIDERED SAFE ENOUGH
TO BE ASKED, BUT YOU'RE NOT
DECREPIT ENOUGH
TO TURN 'EM DOWN

2-5

Smythe